Conten

CW00417541

Foreword: Setting the scene.

Sat quietly above the bridge on Rodanbraes Path or peering out from the top of The Binn above Burntisland on the shores of the Firth of Forth, it is reasonable to start the story of the geology of the area some 350 million years ago, when most of what is spied first appeared; but of course in very different circumstances. Even so events had been conspiring to dramatically change the outlook for a hundred million years and more before that.

This was the era, in the Carboniferous Age, when the great coal reserves were built up throughout Britain, twice as long ago as the coal reserves of Kent, or of the dinosaurs, or of the development of North Sea oil and gas reserves, and of course vastly older than the appearance of man that followed from the small mammals that succeeded the dinosaurs hundreds of millions of years after these events. It was also twice as old as the volcanic series that formed the Great Glen, Mull and Skye, welding the ancient Canadian Shield rocks to the Western Highlands.

Indeed, Fife was part of a massive continent of EurAmerica, with northern Scotland thousands of miles away and Florida far to the south in another continent. Most of Britain, an integral part of the continent, was on the vulnerable continental edge colliding headlong into the southern land mass of Godwana, across a closing ocean, throwing up mountains and possibly the greatest number of volcanoes that remain evident in Britain.

So most of what we see was, at this time, a closing tropical sea, sat across the equator, sometimes huge blue-green turbid lagoons of tropical algae, sometimes clear Coral Seas, sometimes a huge river delta of bright red sand and sometimes driven sand dunes of a vast desert. The oldest coal in Britain is seen below the lavas and much later came the much more extensive organic swamps of Coal Measure ferns of the

Fife Coalfield. But for fifty million years there were volcanoes, thought to be reasonably quietly spewing, forming 430 metres thickness of vast beds of basaltic lavas, ashes and tuffs in thick and consistent layers, inter spaced with sandstone and limestone deposits, shales and thin coal.

Later the mountains were warn down by erosion to some 160 metres of residual volcanic rocks. Volcanoes, mainly dolerite from the Earth's mantle, of similar basic rock types but more crystalline than their basaltic lavas, were everywhere – The Binn, the Kingswood fissures, Arthur's Seat, Orrock Quarry, Bass Rock, Largo Law, Lomond Hills and a hundred more.

Dramatic as the volcanoes were, the story of the Binnend and Burntisland Oil Shale Works lies in a 2 metre seam of shale, geologically some distance below the lavas, but greatly affected by the volcano of The Binn and lava ridges now towering over it and the later extensive intrusion of volcanic sills.

The shale contained oil at up to 30% by weight and its exploitation, over just 16 years resulted in the building of mines, a refinery, candle works, railway and two villages, and then their decline. It resulted in serious pollution of Kinghorn Loch and other burns. Now it provides a wealth of industrial archaeology in stunning settings of Whinnyhall and The Binn and the wonderfully recovered Kinghorn Loch, providing water sports, recreations, bird watching and wildlife in relatively unspoilt woodland and hills and volcanic ridges.

This story argues that without the Scottish Oil Industry, whales and seals may have been driven to extinction by human thirst for lamp and other oils that, at last gasp, became available in huge quantities from oil shale, before liquid oil from wells became widely available from USA and Russia.

Introduction

So, what have these pictures got in common?

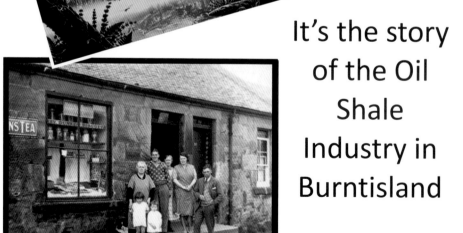

It's the story of the Oil Shale Industry in Burntisland

Map showing locations and features referred to.

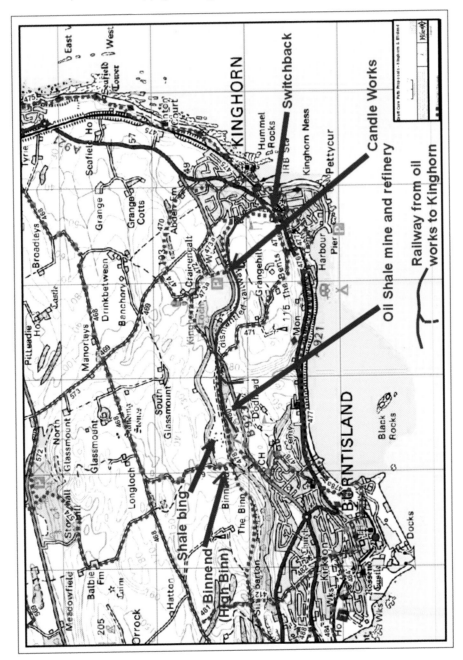

1: Saving the Whale

The early oil industry stopped the need to kill whales and seals for their oil.

By 1880's the slaughter of whales was a disaster.

Although liquid oil occurred throughout the world and tar pits were exploited for oil, the mineral oil industry only took off on a major scale in the 1800s with the refining of bituminous coals but blossomed once oil shales could be exploited and refined. In its hey-day period from 1850 the main area producing oil products was the central belt of Scotland, primarily in Mid and West Lothian, but also into Fife at Burntisland. The oil shale industry led the world, but by 1890 American and Russian liquid oil wells were producing oil much more cheaply and in large quantity.

By 1864 the use of oil lamps had increased greatly for domestic and industrial lighting. There was also increasing demand for lubricating oils in industry. By this time, the early oil industry, pioneered by James (Paraffin) Young, was producing millions of gallons of paraffin per year (by 1886) to light our homes together with a vast array of other products.

Up until this time the major source of oil was from marine mammals, mainly whales, and the whaling industry was seriously over-exploiting a diminishing resource. Sperm Whales produced the best oil, a clean, odourless paraffin oil that was ideal for the fashionable Vienna lamps that lit well-off homes.

In 1816 one British vessel (of an estimated 700 ships) landed 40 whales, but by 1860s only 18 to 216 whales a year were landed by the whole of the British whaling fleet. Turning to Hair Seals, 875,000 were killed annually and by the 1880's the situation was disastrous [1].

Extracts [1] to show how the whale declined but saved from extinction in the nick of time:

Whales Were Considered to Be Swimming Oil Wells

By the late 1700s whale oil was being used to make candles which were smokeless and odourless, a vast improvement over the candles in use before that time. Whale oil obtained from rendering the blubber of a whale, was also used to lubricate precision machine parts. In a sense, a 19th century whaler regarded a whale as a swimming oil well. And the oil from whales, used in machinery, made the industrial revolution possible.

In the 1800s Whaling Became an Industry

By the early 1800s, New Bedford, Massachusetts, became known as the "The City that Lit the World", where 400 of the world's 700 whaling boats visited, but it was a worldwide enterprise. By the 1840's the industry was faltering and whales faced extinction.

Whaling Declined, Yet Lives On in Literature

The Golden Age of whaling extended into the 1850s, and what spelled its demise was the invention of the oil well. With oil extracted from the ground being refined into kerosene for lamps, the demand for whale oil plummeted. And while whaling continued, as whalebone could still be used for a number of household products, the era of the great whaling ships faded into history.

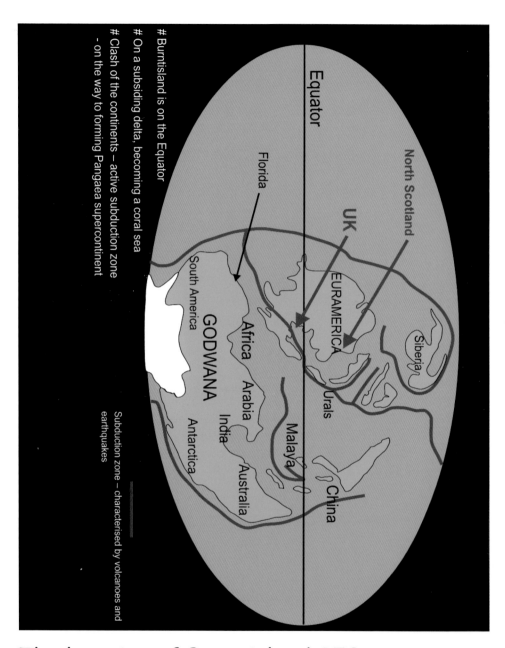

The location of Burntisland 350m years

2: Burntisland: 350 million years ago [2]

During the previous Devonian era, primitive fish abounded in the warm seas and by the early Carboniferous era these had developed into amphibians who crawled onto land and soon giant dragonflies flew in the air.

The geology around the Firth of Forth is described by Scottish Natural Heritage in "Fife and Tayside, a landscape fashioned by geology" [2]. Britain was on the equator and directly in the way of two colliding supercontinents – causing 50 million years of deep seated volcanic activity originating (for Fife) from the Earth's mantle.

The rocks of the Burntisland and Kinghorn area belong to the Carboniferous age, as the supercontinent of Euramerica crashed into the remaining world supercontinent of Godwana.

The oceanic and then warm Coral Seas of this massive equatorial sea, confined on three sides by land, moved between tropical rain forest, swamp, desert and marine conditions. The clash of the continents caused one of the highest concentrations of volcanoes known in Britain as magma rose from the mantle to spew out hundreds of metres thickness of lava and volcanic ashes. These eruptions were mostly quiet and not violent. During the previous 100 million years, the seas had started to team with primitive fish and eventually these came onto land and took to the air, precursors to birds. By 350 million years ago, rampant blue-green (or other) algae inhabited warm lagoons and eventually, together with other plants, formed deposits below occasional encroachment of beds of basalt lavas and interleaving with volcanic sills and vents.

The hot conditions and 'food' source formed oil rather than the thick coal deposits of the later terrestrial swamps to the north. This oil was buried and concentrated into a mound in the rock (anticline) and over millions of years turned to solid bituminous matter in the muddy deposits forming oil shale through West Lothian to Burntisland.

The geology is very complex with lava and tuff beds overlying muddy and sand sediments and the underlying sandstones and limestones invaded and baked by intrusive volcanic sills and necks. Volcanic vents of dolerite formed many of the hills we see today;The Binn, Orrock and the fissure volcano of Kingswood, are local volcanoes. A detailed account of volcanic rock types and geomorphology is described by A.R.MacGregor [3].

By 325 million years ago tropical rain forests built up on the coastal plains eventually forming thick coal measures of the Fife Coalfield.

Concept of The Binn volcano and Kingswood fissure volcano, land or sea, then murky swamp, then coral sea interrupted by lava flow after lava flow.

Tropical Rain Forest, sordid lakes, and volcanoes

Equatorial lakes and seas smothered with algae – forming organic detritus buried and compressed into oily deposits.

Baked and retorted at depth by heat of the adjacent 'Binn' voloanic magma.

Present day geology

Pink shows each lava bed.
Red volcanic plug and green sills baked oil from below.

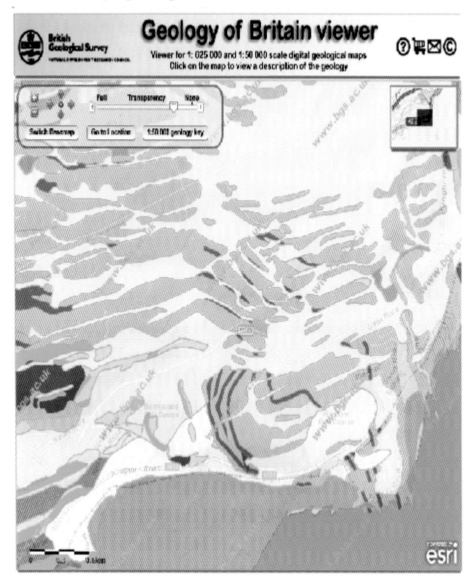

http://www.bgs.ac.uk/discoveringGeology/geologyOfBritain
/viewer.html

 **_Burntisland Oil Shale Field_**

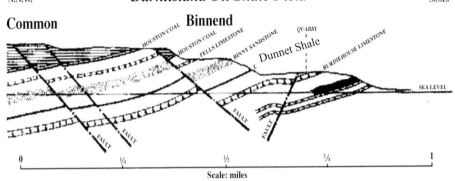

Scale: miles

Reference (29).

The immediate area of geology is described as the Burdiehouse (Burntisland) Limestone and Oil-shale Group (Dunnet Shale)[4] shown above as the "Binnend Oil Shale Field". The succession of rocks in the formation presents a remarkable insight into the volcanic turmoil that existed and is dramatically shown by the succession of formations exhibited along the Fife Coastal Path between Burntisland and Kirkcaldy. The study section east of Kinghorn is described in a teachers guide[8].

The succession[4] is made extremely complex by uplift, faulting, folding and the injection of sills and vents. It developed along the coast on either side of Burntisland, whence it stretches inland for five miles and westwards along the coast as far as Charlestown. The structure is dominated by an anticlinal fold in Midlothian, parallel with the Pentland Hills which meets Fife at Burntisland and then strikes north north east. Upper Silurian and Lower Old Red Sandstone rocks are brought up to the surface, while the various members of the Carboniferous system are thrown off on either side.

At Brosyhall there was a sandstone quarry while the Burdiehouse Limestone was quarried at Dodhead. Above the Burdiehouse Limestone is the top class Grange Sandstone over 35 metres thick and used to construct the New Town in Edinburgh.

Above this is found the Dunnet Shales containing a 2 metre seam of oil shale east of The Binn volcanic vent. The softer Binnend Sandstone follows, then the 350 mm thick Houston Coal seam.

The oil shale is in two sections separated by considerable faulting. It was found to dip a little to the west of north at an angle of about 10°, and was followed by a mine driven a little east from Binnend along the dip for about 900 metres to a point about 200 metres north east of Common. About 350 metres from the mouth of the mine a fault was encountered, running in an east north east direction, with a downthrow of 20 metres to the south. About 330 metres further north another dislocation was met with, trending east-west with a downthrow of 160 metres to the south. The shale was worked eastwards as far as the Gallowhill Plantation, where it was found to be inclined towards east south east under the volcanic ridge.

The seam follows from the eastern margin of The Binn agglomerate parallel with that of the limestone below it. It is thrown down by a fault which runs in a north-easterly direction from the old limestone quarry of Brosyhall, where its position is seen, to the lava-sheets at Rodanbraes. But the outcrop immediately resumes its previous course, until below Whinnyhall it wheels round with the limestone and strikes southward in the direction of the shore at Kingswood.

The remaining lavas amount to some 120 metre thickness in five flows, but also includes the intrusions over wide areas and the magma vents themselves.

According to W.M.Stephen[10] the Dunnet Shale that contains the Oil Shale at Binnend is 6ft 3 inches (1.8 metre) thick and the east (No 3 & 4 mines, towards Kingswood) and west sections (No 1& 2 mines) were separated by a fault. The shale followed for 900 metres by No 1 and 2 mines dipped to the NNW by some 15 degrees and ended 600-700 ft (180-210 metres) below ground level. No 3 mine reached a depth of 715 ft (215 metres) below ground level. No 4 pit was never fully exploited. The western seam was seriously affected by The Binn volcanic vent.

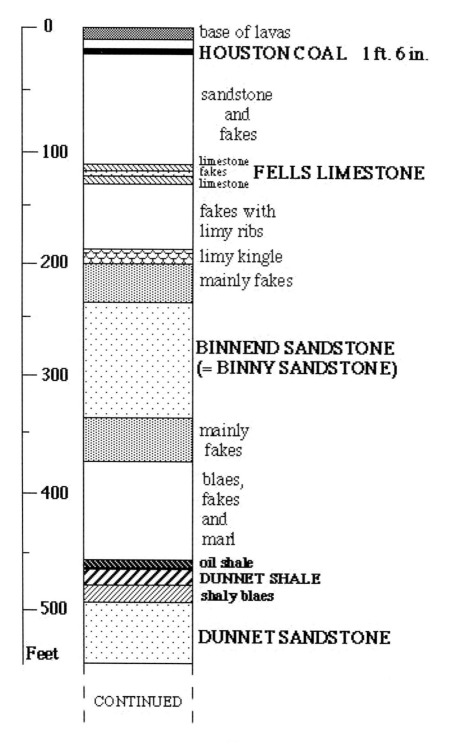

base of lavas

HOUSTON COAL   1 ft. 6 in.

sandstone
    and
    fakes

limestone
fakes   FELLS LIMESTONE
limestone

fakes with
limy ribs

limy kingle

mainly fakes

BINNEND SANDSTONE
(= BINNY SANDSTONE)

mainly
  fakes

blaes,
fakes
and
marl

oil shale
DUNNET SHALE
shaly blaes

DUNNET SANDSTONE

0

100

200

300

400

500

Feet

CONTINUED

13

Some geological features on the Fife Coastal Path east of Kinghorn.

- based on locations described in Scottish Earth Science Education Forum[8].
- typical of the rock formations and sequences in the Binnend area.

Basalt lava beds showing columnar structure.

Erosion of tops of columns showing 'false' pillow lava structure

Lava beds laid down over limestone and sandstone beds

Basalt lava bed laid down over an arid red earth deposit

Lava bed orientated with Salisbury Crags and Arthur's Seat (in the distance on south shore of Firth of Forth)

60 metre thickness of volcanic ash and tuff

Burdiehouse Limestone with club moss fossil (grew to 40m).

Courtesy http://upload.wikimedia.org/wikipedia/commons/3/3f/Lepidophloios.JPG

Binnend Sandstone

Orrock Quarry - Dolerite volcanic vent

What do you see today?

Every south facing ridge around Kinghorn Loch, Rodanbraes and The Binn are formed of basalt (whin) lava beds. Dolerite forms most of the vent rocks. There are several quarries of high quality building stone - limestones and sandstones - used in the building of the New Town in Edinburgh, and still used for restoration work.

The Binn, Orrock Quarry, Dunearn, Kingswood End, Lomond Hills, Largo Law, Arthur's Seat, North Berwick Law, Bass Rock, and many more are old volcanic necks.

Looking down over Burntisland from the top of The Binn

Lomond Hills (volcanic vents)

3: Oil Shale

The organic components of oil shale derive from a variety of organisms, such as the remains of algae, spores, pollen, plant cuticles and corky fragments of herbaceous and woody plants, and cellular debris from other aquatic and land plants (Wilkipedia [5]).

Oil shale reserves are double that of oil (Wilkipedia [5]).

The term oil shale generally refers to any sedimentary rock that contains solid bituminous materials (called kerogen) that are released as petroleum-like liquids when the rock is heated in the chemical process of pyrolysis[6,9]. The organic detritus was incorporated in mud and silt at the bottom of lagoons, lakes or quiet seas some 350 million years ago. Over long periods of time, heat and pressure transformed the materials into oil shale in a process similar to the process that forms oil; however, the heat and pressure were not as great. The oil gathered and concentrated under the anticline to form high quality kerogen. The shale contains enough oil that it will burn without any additional processing, and it is known as "the rock that burns".

Oil shale was mined and processed to generate oil similar to oil pumped from conventional oil wells; however, extracting oil from oil shale is more complex than conventional oil recovery and therefore more expensive. The oil substances in oil shale are solid and cannot be pumped directly out of the ground. The oil shale is heated to a high temperature (a process called retorting) and fractionated to give various products. Sulphate of ammonia and various inorganic chemicals are also produced in abundance[6].

In general, the precursors of the organic matter in oil shale and coal also differ. Much of the organic matter in oil shale is of algal origin, but may also include remains of vascular land plants that more commonly compose much of the organic matter in coal. The origin of some of the organic matter in oil shale is obscure because of the lack of recognizable biologic structures that would help identify the precursor organisms. Such materials may be of bacterial origin or the product of bacterial degradation of algae or other organic matter [7].

Oil Shale

The oil shale at Binnend is the richest in Britain being up to 30% oil and there is still plenty of it left – especially under Grangehill and Burntisland Golf Course[10].

4: History of the Oil Industry in Scotland and the Burntisland works

Development of the industry in Scotland.

Becker & Serle's patent for producing pitch and tar from coal in 1681, led to its use in Naval ships [10]. The Earl of Dundonald produced a patent in 1781 for the distillation of coal, which led to gas making from the early nineteenth century. James and John Young of Glasgow imported and later mass produced the "Vienna" lamp in the 1850s. There was also a growing need for lubricating oils for cast iron machinery in industry.

James "Paraffin" Young was born in 1811. In 1848 he was asked to investigate an oil spring in Alfreton, Derbyshire, and erected a works to refine paraffin, lighting fuel and lubricating oils, but the spring failed within two years. In 1850 he took out a patent for the distillation of coal and began to exploit a poor coal, Torbanite, in Bathgate giving 600 litres of oil per tonne. With American imports, prices dropped from 3/6d a gallon to 4d a gallon at the dockside and a price war and undercutting ensued. Henderson's retort of 1873 improved efficiency and Young & Bailby retort in 1882 almost doubled sulphate of ammonia recovery, a very valuable by-product, but this improvement was never employed at Burntisland.

Development of the industry at Burntisland

Before 1878.

George Simpson (based in Edinburgh) had processed some oil shale from Binnend.

1878 to 1881.

With a partner he set up the Binnend Oil Company to expand operations.

1881 to 1892 .

John Waddell bought the company and set up the Burntisland Oil Company. The prospectus was quite extensive in both land and minerals:

> "This company has been formed with the purpose of purchasing the Estates of Whinnyhall, Binnend, Common, Rodanbraes, Kinghorn Loch, Lochlands and parts of Craigencur and Galahill, near Burntisland, containing Shale, Coal, Limestone, and Freestone, and also the Oil Works erected thereon, and for completing and enlarging the present Oil Works"[13]

By 1884 production was booming:

> "Symptoms of prosperity continue to characterise the Burntisland Oil Company's works in the the neighbourhood. New shale pits have been sunk with excellent results, and two additional benches of retorts, with refining accessories, are now in course of erection. Fully 600 hands are now employed and the existing house accommodation has been found inadequate.[14]

The Candle Works and railway followed::

"The Binnend Oil Company has acquired from Kinghorn Town Council a piece of ground near the Loch to erect a candle factory. Operations to start immediately. Proximity to the new railway; which is being rushed forward, and the loch burn required for cooling purposes has determined the choice of site."[15]

In its heyday it produced 500 tonne of oil share giving 75,000 litres of paraffin (kerosene) plus candle wax, lubricating oils, other light oils, bitumen and tar and (very profitably) sulphate of ammonia fertiliser. Nearly 1,000 men were employed. Initially excellent dividends were provided to shareholders until 1887 when 7% was offered. After this production became more uncertain and men laid off at times until it ceased in 1892. There was the prospect of developing the huge resources under Grangehill (owned by Philp Trust) but the oil shale industry could not compete with oil wells and the company went into liquidation.

After 1892.

By 1893 only 50 workers remained and despite forming a new company no production occurred. The works (other than Candle Works) was dismantled in 1894 and liquidated in 1905.

From 1894 to 1898 plant and machinery and the workers houses were put up for sale, and much of the machinery and an extensive supply of candles and wax were sold.

References: Fisk[11] and Sommerville[12]

5: Mining the oil shale.

The works in its heyday.

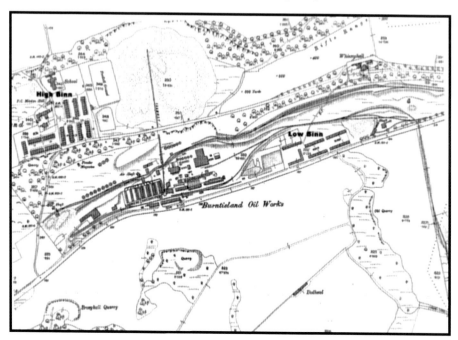

Extent of working

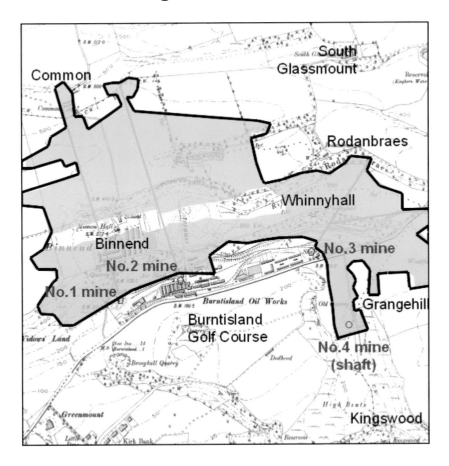

The mine stretched from the fractured rock close to The Binn volcanic rocks to Gallowhill at the head of Kinghorn Loch and 900 metres north to Common. The mine workings were some 2 metres in height and descended some 200-300 metres below ground level as they followed the rock.

Before closure the owners negotiated a lease with the Philp Trust to take the mine further under Grangehill in a huge expansion. However market economics were against them.

Mining[(16)]

Adapted by Harry Knox from his book "The Scottish Shale Oil Industry & The Mineral Railway Lines"

Shale mining was hard, manual work. The miner took an agreed payment for the amount of shale extracted by him during his shift. Agreements varied depending on good times or bad. An average day's work produced around three tons of shale or more per man, or linear progress of around 12 feet per week into the seam. The miner employed helpers and paid for his gunpowder (black powder).

At the shale face (the workplace) the Miner made the holes in the shale into which the explosives were firmly placed, for firing. Early picks were replaced by hand operated ratchet drills comprising a screw drill which was worked back and forward to required depth. The drill body was supported on a suitably placed pit prop, (a boring tree). Into these holes, the Miner inserted cartridges of explosive contained in strong paper tubes. When the explosive was firmly lodged in the hole and had been stopped up by a "paste" of shale dust and water, a fuse was inserted and lit by the Miner, generally from the flame on his lamp. After the shots were fired, sufficient time was left for the fumes to clear before the shovellors (Drawers) began to load the broken shale into the hutches. When full, the Drawer would push the hutch out to a haulage level where it, along with other loaded hutches were transported in trains, hauled by a winding engine out of the mine adit to the surface. Each hutch carried an identification tag, and on reaching the surface, the tonnage was credited to that Miner. Winding engines were used extensively to move hutches on the very steep site, which proved to be a most dangerous activity.

The actual mining teams of two or three men, were supported by the "on-cost" men. These were men not immediately involved in mining shale, but who followed on behind the mining operation by "brushing" the headings created, that is putting up proper supports for the roof, and removing any waste.

Stoop and Room Working

Mining at Binnend was by Stoop and Room working. A series of headings, around 4 metres wide and 2-3 metres high were driven into the seams of shale at 4 to 5 metre intervals. As each workplace progressed, at about 4 to 5 metres depending on the inclination of the seam, cross headings were driven leaving pillars of shale around 4-5 metres square as roof supports. These pillars were the Stoops. The levels and workplaces were the Rooms.

Once an area was worked out the stoops were steadily removed to gain all the oil shale and gradually the workings would close up through collapse ("stooped"). The mine was unusual in that the stoops were often removed on nearer works before deeper ones were worked out.

The Mines and Pit

Number 1, 2 and 3 mines were adits, levels taken from the surface at an angle to follow the seam. Hutches were removed in trains by winding engines at the surface. Number 4 pit was a vertical shaft sunk down to access the seam of shale.

Hutches were run on a pair of narrow gauge rails with ropes strung around the winding engines.

The Use of Hutches

Hutches (see photograph) were extensively used on the surface too. Hot waste retorted shale was hauled from the retorts through cooling water (which reached boiling point) and then up the steep hillside to the bings. This was the source of several fatal accidents.

Stoop and Room working.

FIG. I

SHALE WORKINGS — BINNEND

TTTT AREAS OF ROOMS
▨ AREAS STOOPED
×93 DEPTHS IN FATHOMS

| 440 YARDS |

Walter M Stephen[10].

Courtesy of Museum of the Scottish Shale Mine Industry[16].

Hutches

Oil shale was blasted with black powder and manually loaded onto hutches, which were pushed to a central point where they were connected together and hauled to the surface by a stationery winding engine.

Hutches were used to move shale and waste throughout the works.

Picture from Clydeside Images.

The mine wagons or hutches shown here are from a 19th century coal mine in Coatbridge.

Winding

The winding engines comprised large wooden wheels on an axle and driven by a stationary steam engine in a masonry built engine house,   over which a continuous rope ran. Loaded or retuning hutches could be fixed to this continuous rope. The ropes may have been of rope or wire.

Accidents

There appears to have been relatively few fatal accidents at Burntisland works for that era – perhaps it was a well managed works.

Many accidents were caused by runaway hutches because of the steep gradients involved.
Reported fatal incidents:
James Dunachie (1886) killed by hutches whilst trespassing.
Thomas Cullen (1886) when a hauling rope broke.
Frank Morgan (1888) killed by roof fall.
Patrick Kelly killed by a hutch in No.1 mine in 1891. A miner, Hugh Linch, was put on trial charged with culpable homicide. He was accused of failing to attach a wagon correctly so that it ran

downhill and crushed Patrick Kelly, who died soon afterwards[11]. There were also at least three injuries and one fatality from failed shot firings. One of the incidents occurred in Mine No. 2, when two men went to examine a shot that had not gone off. One of the men suffered severe head injuries, and had to be taken to

Edinburgh Royal Infirmary by ferry across the Firth of Forth[11].

In 1892, No.1 mine suffered a major fire and a major roof fall which was expensive to clear. Mining was suspended, but there is no record of any casualties resulting from the fire[11].

Water Control

All underground workings, by their very nature, suffered from the ingress of water to a greater or smaller extent. There was no real alternative to providing pumps to control water levels and steam driven pumps were employed.

Explosives

Black powder (gunpowder), packed in stout paper tubes of varying lengths and weights, was the preferred explosive used in shale mining. It was an effective way of splitting and breaking the shale without shattering it into unusable sizes. The black powder consisted of 75 parts of saltpetre, 15 parts of carbon and 10 parts of sulphur. A secure explosives magazine was located at a safe distance from the mine entrances.

The explosive was ignited by inserting "strum", a rope like fuse with a black powder core, into the cartridge. The Miner lit the fuse, either with a chemical igniter or merely by applying the flame on his lamp to the end of the strum. Shot-firing with black powder created noxious fumes and this was an ongoing source of complaint. Even with very efficient methods of ventilation, it could take some time before the air could be cleared. The means of ventilating the mines has not been ascertained.

Lighting / Illumination

Underground workings were extremely dark places. The illumination was from the lamp carried by the men in their caps. In the early days, these lamps, shaped like very small kettles, used animal fat (tallow) as a fuel. The tallow was softened by holding and rolling it in the hands and was then pushed into the container. A wick ran the length of the spout, and when this was lit, it burned with a rather obnoxious smelling flame. This was known as a naked light lamp. These lamps were gradually replaced by acetylene lamps, a more substantial lamp in two parts. The lower part was a container into which calcium carbide was placed, and the upper part was a water reservoir. When the water,was allowed to drip on to the carbide, it produced acetylene. This gas escaped through a small nozzle where it was lit, and provided a source of lighting, but it was again, a naked flame lamp. These lamps were generally hooked into the miners cloth cap. There was however, one further lamp which was widely used, being a legal requirement, and that was the Safety Lamp.

6: Extracting and refining the oil ⁽¹⁶⁾

Adapted by Harry Knox from his book "The Scottish Shale Oil Industry & The Mineral Railway Lines"

Shale Retorts

The retort design had evolved over the life of the industry and it is a fact that the Scottish oil companies led the world in this retort technology. The first retorts to be used at Bathgate by James Young, were horizontal "D"-shaped common retorts. With the expiration of Dr. Young's Patent, so the search for more efficient types of retort began. The most common design of retort thereafter, was to be the vertical retort. Various engineers employed within the industry applied their thinking to improving retort design and retort performance.

The earliest type of vertical retort was designed by A.C. Kirk, but was obsolete by 1883 and replaced at Binnend by the Henderson Retorts.

Norman Macfarlane Henderson, Manager of Oakbank Paraffin Oil Works, designed a retort that provided a more efficient heating process for the shale, and offering a greater throughput of shale and yield of far higher quantities of related products. Retorts were set up in banks (benches) of 60 retorts per bench and mass production was well and truly established. The retort house is shown as "B" in the figure that follows.

Crushing the Shale

Once the shale had been mined it was first put through a crusher. This was a series of steel rollers fitted with specially hardened metal teeth, which reduced the shale into fairly uniform 100 mm cubed pieces. This made the raw shale easier to load in to the retorts and ensured the uniformity of heating as the shale descended by gravity down the length of the retort.

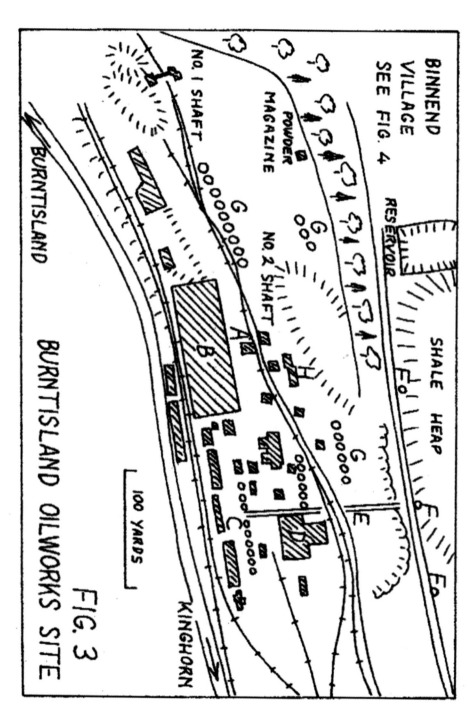

From Walter M Stephen [10]

33

Crude Oil Production

The crushed shale was taken by hutch to the top of the retort bench and loaded into a steel hopper at the top of each retort, and each hopper was charged around every 6 hours. The shale then passed, by gravity, into the upper part of the retort, a cast iron vertical tube (later of steel) around 3.5 metre in length and about 0.6 metre in diameter. The retorts were arranged in sets within a common firebrick heating chamber. When in the retort, the shale was then subjected to continuous heat from an external source with the temperature in the upper portion being around 132°C and increasing to around 250°C at the bottom of the cast iron section. The shale, still moving down by gravity, then passed into the lower firebrick portion of the retort, this being around 6 metres in length and increasing in diameter to about 1 metre. Here, the heat applied became more intense, ranging from 500°C through to 1000°C. In this lower stage, water and air were injected into the retort with about 350 litres of water being added to each ton of shale. This water provided the hydrogen necessary to create ammonia from the nitrogen released by the shale. This also created superheated steam which both increased and stabilised the temperature of the shale throughout the diameter of the retort to protect the ammonia and oil vapours from further "cracking" or decomposition, thus ensuring an oil of the highest quality. These oil vapours were swept up from the lower part of the retort into a large diameter outlet pipe passing through the neck of the retort and onwards into the atmospheric condensers.

The burnt shale inside the retort was held for about 4 hours in most retorts. The spent shale, at the completion of the retorting process, passed down into a cast iron chamber where it was discharged into a hopper by a rotating steel arm. From the discharge point the spent shale was loaded into hutches to be taken by a continuous rope haulage system to the waste tip.

The heating of the retorts, was achieved by burning the flammable gases given off by the shale under heating, to supplement the coal gas produced "in house" at the oil works. The burning gases were swept upwards in a spiraling flow through the heating chambers providing a continuous heating and finally escaping into the atmosphere through the chimneys on top of the retorts. The crude oil and ammoniacal liquid, having passed through the condensers was then separated where the crude oil, being lighter, rose to the surface and was drawn off via a pipe leading to a receiver.

The ammoniacal liquid,settled to the bottom of the separator and was drawn off in to another separate receiver. Any gases from the condensers were cooled and scrubbed by water to recover any remaining ammonia and naphtha.

Recovery of Naphtha

The scrubbed gas from the scrubbing tower, was sprayed with shale gas oil which then absorbed any naphtha present. This oil / naphtha mixture was passed into a naphtha still with steam and any naphtha present condensed back into unrefined naphtha. The gases were also cooled and re-circulated back into the scrubbing process which was a continuous process.

Around 15 litres of naphtha per tonne of shale were recovered.

Recovery of Ammonia

The ammonia present in the gases was scrubbed with water in a scrubbing tower. The ammonia recovered by this process, plus the ammonia obtained from the retort condensers was mixed. The ammonia, now expelled as a vapour, was absorbed in dilute sulphuric acid and when evaporated left sulphate of ammonia in a crystalline form.

Refining Crude Oil

The crude oil was further treated to effect separation into a range of hydrocarbons of differing boiling points and properties, crude solid wax separated and impurities removed. This gave a range of safe, useful refined products at best price.

The crude oil remaining, at the first refining stage, was heated in a still and separation of each fraction was achieved by condensing the oil vapours at the differing boiling points and leading the condensed liquid oils into separate receivers, the vapours of those with the lower boiling points distilling over the first stages and those with the higher boiling points distilling over the latter stages. Steam was used in this process to facilitate the distillation of the various fractions and also to control the temperature to avoid any further decomposition of the products. A by-product of this process was a heavy, impure tar which was itself then burned to provide the necessary heat in this distillation process .The vertical steel stills (post 1883) were far from perfect and continued to give problems which led to the industry later adopting pot or coking stills. The Henderson continuous boiler still reduced the distillation process to a single stage.

Refining Crude Oil: Second Distillation

The "green oil" obtained from the first distillation was again run through a similar distillation but no steam was employed in this stage. **Crude burning oil, heavy oil and paraffin** are produced.

The crude oil was then washed with sulphuric acid to remove nitrogen compounds and to stabilise the final products, before being washed in caustic soda solution. After settling, the oil was re-distilled in fine old boilers (boiler stills). At this stage with the residue being run off continuously, the fractions obtained were **Lamp oil and Power oil, Lighthouse oil and Residuum**

At this point the residuum was blown into a separate single boiler still and re-distilled to produce **Heavy burning oil, Light gas oil and Heavy gas oil**

The heavy oils and paraffin were refrigerated and treated with liquid ammonia, and when at the required temperature, the cold oil was forced, under pressure, into a series of filter presses of increasing compression, forcing all the remaining liquid oil to be collected in another container. The filter press cakes of paraffin wax were then further pressed in linen or cotton cloth until only solid cakes of paraffin wax remained. This **paraffin wax** was removed for further refining.

The liquid oil remaining after this pressing process was termed blue oil and treated with a solution of acid and caustic soda, and, when finally settled, was collected and re-distilled in the blue oil stills, to produce **Heavy gas oil, Cleaning oil, Lubricating oil and Residuum.** The residuum was again drawn off and prepared for the markets as oil residuum, for the manufacture of **greases and wire-rope lubricant.**

The **gas-oil, cleaning and lubricating oils** were further treated for market.

Crude Solid Paraffin Wax

This crude paraffin wax was subjected to a sweating process in a large, purpose-built sweat house each of which equipped with close-fitting iron doors and internally fitted with steam coils along the walls. These houses also contained a series of water-cooled horizontal pans. The raw melted wax was run into these pans from a charging tank above the building and when the wax had been cooled by the water, and solidified once more, the sweating process began. When the wax was once more in a liquid state due to the steam heating, the wax was clarified and impurities removed by absorbing colour with Fullers Earth or charcoal. The wax was cooled once more, then re-liquidised by sweating once more, yielding a fine, soft wax and a hard paraffin wax of good clear colour, with a melting point of around 50°C. This wax was for candle making. The candles produced from this wax were of exceptionally high quality, burning with an extremely bright light.

The Refined Products

Spirits and Naphtha

Various spirits were produced over the years to meet changing market requirements, such as **motor spirit, extracting spirit, solvent naphtha** (used in rubber-making and waterproofing), **burning naphtha, white spirit** (used in the manufacture of paint) and **solvents** used in the manufacture of linoleum.

Lamp and Power Oil

Lamp oil was in great demand, particularly by the Railway Companies, as a continuously burning oil for use in signal lamps and train lamps. The Scottish Railway companies contracted to purchase lamp oil from the various oil companies, each taking about 25,000 gallons (120,000 litres) every two months. The lighthouse oil was, with its high flash point, a safe oil to use to store in quantity.

Gas / Fuel Oil and Cleaning Oil

Gas oil was just another grade of fuel oil. The fuel oils (furnace fuel oils) were widely used in steam boilers as an alternative to coal, particularly in sea-going vessels. The fuel oil fuelled the ships of the Royal Navy during WWI.

Cleaning oil was a highly refined oil much in demand by railway companies for cleaning locomotives. It was also used in the manufacture of axle grease.

Batching Oil

This particular grade of oil was specially prepared for the spinning industry. It was used, in the main, in Dundee for jute spinning and in Lancashire in the cotton spinning trade. Mixed with water and sprayed over the fibres during the spinning process, it kept them soft and flexible, thus preventing breakage.

Lubricating Oil

Used to lubricate all sorts of machinery and was used in the manufacture of specialised greases.

Residuum Oil

This thick oil residue was a constituent part of heavy lubricating greases.

Production of Sulphuric Acid

The sulphuric acid used in the refining process was made in-house from iron pyrites imported from Spain, burned in air, to produce sulphur dioxide gas. Oxidation of the gas with sodium nitrate produced dilute sulphuric acid which was concentrated to an 80% acid.

Coopers at Broxburn.

7: The Candle Works, Kinghorn

The Burntisland Oil Company was one of a number of smaller shale oil companies that produced its own candles.
This blue card with an engraved label was presumably the top of a box of candles. The lettering reads "Burntisland Holyrood Paraffin Candles. 8s. Burntisland Oil Co Ltd." the main illustration is of Holyrood palace with images of ornate candlesticks and the trademark of the Burntisland company; a star with an oil barrel in the centre.

Image Courtesy of SCRAN

Prior to its conversion to the Candle Works the works was owned by Swan Brothers who had the Upper, Mid and St Leonard's Flax Mills and Tyrie Bleachfields in Kinghorn and 13500 spindles and 1160 workers in Fife and Dundee together with ships for export. The company went bankrupt in 1886.

The Upper Mill was rebuilt and opened as the new Candle Works in 1887. This produced paraffin burning oil and wax, lubricating oils and sulphate of ammonia. There were probably 200-300 men employed at the Candle Works. It closed in 1894.

The process, by law, required careful refining of the crude wax and paraffin and this is evidenced by the number of fatal fires caused by less safe American lamp oil (in 1895 in London there were 3633 fires from lamps accounting for 25% of all fire related deaths).

8: The railway.

A railway built in 1886, and opened 1887 with the Candle Works, travelling from no. 1,2 and 3 Mines and Refinery at Binnend and a branch to No.4 pit in 1891, to Kinghorn Station.

It had a steep gradient up to 1 in 50, especially at Kinghorn. There was a re-entrant (switchback) at Viewforth Place and there may have been a stationery engine and hawser here to help the heavy trains enter the station safely. It transported more than 200 tonnes of product each day. Although a problem for operations, the re-entrant reduced the gradient of the line and could safely derail trains or prevent a heavy train crashing onto the main line.

Indeed it was reported in the Edinburgh Evening News of 9th February 1889, that three wagons loaded with coal on their way to the oil works broke loose from the engine at Kinghorn Loch and went down the incline and smashed into pieces, scattering the coal, near the switchback.

9: Environmental Pollution.

Pollution of Kirkton Burn through Burntisland

The Kirkton Burn evidently suffered badly from the Oil Shale works, with permanent pollution of its waters. It is a small stream with no abstraction or use.

However, In 1880 Robert Kirke complained about pollution in the stream running through his property and the offensive smell from the works. He tried unsuccessfully to halt production at the works, but the company eased the pollution problem by laying a waste pipe from the works to the sea [11]. It is unlikely that this would have alleviated the problem due to the many springs in the area.

Protection of Kinghorn Loch

The bed (solum) of Kinghorn Loch was owned by the oil company but the water was owned by Kinghorn Town Council and free to use for the flax mills throughout Kinghorn. The free and effective supply of water to the mills and spinners was essential.

In 1882 the oil company diverted water (presumably at Common) for its use and water stopped flowing to the loch. Investigations found the company had diverted with a 3" pipe and not a 1" pipe to raise steam as they claimed. Kinghorn Town Council were vindicated.

In 1886 when the railway was built, it broke the banks of Whinnyhall lochans and reduced water flow to the loch. It stopped the mills for a while.

In 1887, the Upper Flax Mill of Swan Brothers was sold for the Candle Works and the oil company started abstracting water from the loch without paying for it. Litigation once more.

Fortunately, the oil company did not pollute the loch as badly as it fouled the Kirkton Burn down through Burntisland.
However things were not good and its use as a public supply put in severe jeopardy. On 13th July 1888[17] analysis of the water found it to be of inferior drinking quality, affected by excessive amounts of ammonia and phosphate infected by protozoa making it unfit for dietary purpose.

By 1888 the Police Commission of Kinghorn (of Town Council) [18][19] recommended a clear water reservoir at Common with a pipe to new reservoir and treatment works at Craigencalt, all in iron pipework to Kinghorn. However they were unable to secure the land so the problem with water supply to the burgh, affected by the oil works, remained.

Also since the Candle Works opened it was reported that perch and pike had died in their hundreds[20]. The water supply was certainly in jeopardy and water supplied from Kirkcaldy could not be guaranteed.

A new water supply tank was built by 1916, sorting future problems.

10: Workers and their families.

Please see Walter M Stephen [10] and www.Burntisland.net [12] for more detail.

The company built two new villages, the High and Low Binn, and added to houses at Common.

The High Binn (now referred to as Binnend or Binn Village) was built at Binnend Farm, which already housed workers. It had twelve rows of six or eight stone dwellings of two rooms each. By 1890's there was also a wooden, corrugated steel roofed Mission Hall, Institute (reading room and community hall), football pitch and latterly a school for 220 children.

The Low Binn was seen as the poorer relation and comprised mainly immigrant (Irish) families.

Houses and people.

High Binn

Low Binn

Institute

High Binn
houses

The Binn village survived for many decades after the miners left.
The last resident finally departed in 1954.

Population.

In 1881 only 36 people lived at Binnend Farm.

By 1883 the rural population of Burntisland doubled to 1181 with 100 families at the company villages and by 1886, 1000 persons of all ages.

In 1892, High Binn had 564 inhabitants of 95 houses and Low Binn had 192 people in 33 houses.

Of nearly 1000 workers, 164 lived in Burntisland and 126 in Kinghorn (mainly working at the Candle Works) and 79 boarders.

By 1901 it was less than half with 127 empty houses and by 1961 there were only 161 people living in rural Burntisland.

The High Binn was always regarded as having higher status than the Low Binn. It appears this was the result of a larger proportion of people in the Low Binn having Irish origins .They would have been the victims of the negative stereotypes applied to Irish people throughout much of Britain at that time [11].

The houses were built in terraces of single storey dwellings. Each house had just two rooms, with a total floor area of about 405 square feet. The front door opened on to one room, and you would pass through a door to get to the back room. Each room had a fire place and a window. In some houses the space between the ceiling and the roof could be used as a sleeping area, useful for those who had large families or who took in lodgers [11].

Dan Connaghan[10]

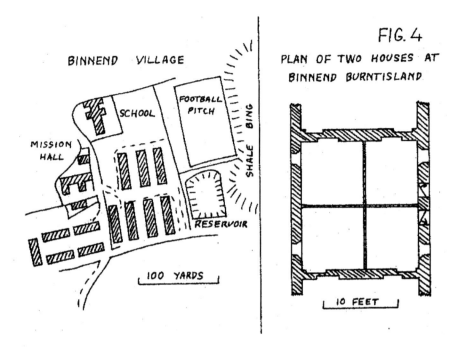

BINNEND VILLAGE

SCHOOL

MISSION HALL

FOOTBALL PITCH

SHALE BING

RESERVOIR

100 YARDS

FIG. 4

PLAN OF TWO HOUSES AT BINNEND BURNTISLAND

10 FEET

Dan and his Burntisland-born wife had five children in a two roomed house. They also had five lodgers, who probably hotbedded.

Standard of living.

Workers at Binnend Oil Works were better paid than in West Lothian, and 5% better than local coal miners. They also had a 'free' shop and newsagent. In 1884 they helped establish the Burntisland Co-operative Society.

In 1883 the workers went on strike for more money and a holiday every five weeks (they won't have worked on Sunday). They were given it without any problem.

By law they worked a maximum eight-hour day.

They had annual excursions for employees.

The workers were considered to have "money-to-burn" and several groups of very worthy entertainers visited Binnend.

11: What remains today? Quite a bit.

The great flue
climbs the cliff face

The tramway tunnel

More remnants

One of the winding houses/stationery engines

Building near No.1 mine entrance

Institute and shop (High Binn)

12: Early History of Whinnyhall (Binnend)

The National Archive of Scotland, in a letter to Kinghorn Historical Society [21] suggests that King William I granted Burgh Status to Kinghorn sometime between 1165 and 1172. The Great Seal reference [22] is a ratification of King David II in 1364, of a charter of confirmation granted by King Alexander II in 1285.

The Common Lands held by the Burgh of Kinghorn stretched from Lochacres in the east, the Mire, many parcels in Kinghorn (including Bowbutts) through Kinghorn Loch to Whinnyhall, Rodanbraes and Common. The all important water supply originated from the Banchory Burn from beyond Common and diverted to Kinghorn Loch as the Loch Burn to supply the mills sometime before 1584, and springs in various places, importantly at the Mire (Ladyburn). The Loch Burn was compromised during the Oil Shale era, as was the Kirkton Burn flowing from Whinnyhall to Burntisland.

Whinnyhall may have been sold by the Burgh at some time but it was sold on by Private Treaty in 1875 [23] as "The desirable estate of Whinnyhall including Binnend, Common, Roddenbraes, Kinghorn Loch and Lochlands". This describes productive wood, three steadings and site for mansion house and grassland and is known to have been hunting grounds (probably with Royal connections to Pettycur) since early times.

George Simpson immediately progressed with the Binnend oil Works but by 1878 offered the land for sale and in 1879 John Waddell set up the Burntisland Oil Company [24] which agreed with reduced mineral right costs to proceed in 1881 with the purchase [25]. By 1896 the company was in liquidation [26] and by 1903 was gone. By 1910 the lands of Whinnyhall were being used for military training [27] and by 1920 the camp was being closed [28]. The estate remained as Crown Estate until sale to British Aluminium.

References

A particular thank you to Iain Sommerville (burntisland.net) and Ian Archibald (Burntisland Heritage Trust) for assistance and editing.

[1] www.about.com, 19th Century History of whaling

[2] SNH, "Fife & Tayside, a landscape fashioned by geology", 2001

[3] MacGregor, A.R. Fife and Angus Geology, 3rd edition, Pentland Press, 1996

[4] Geology of Western and Central Fife and Kinross-shire, 1900

[5] Wilkipedia

[6] US Department of the Interior, Oil Shale and Tar Sands Programmatic EIS Information Center

[7] J R Dyni, "Geology and Resources of Some World Oil-shale Deposits", Reprint of USGS Report 2005-5294, Geology.com

[8] Scottish Earth Science Education Forum, Earth Science Outdoors Teachers Guide: Higher & Intermediate 2: Kinghorn, Fife, 2009 (www.sesef.org.uk)

[9] K.Urov & A.Sumberg, "Characteristics of oil shales, etc", Oil Shale, 1999, 16 (3)

[10] Walter M Stephen, "The Binnend Oil Works and The Binn Village", 1968

[11] S Fisk, Abandoned Communities - Binnend, http://www.abandonedcommunities.co.uk/binnend1.html

[12] Sommerville I, www.burntisland.net/heritage-trust.html

[13] The Scotsman, 20th August 1881

[14] The Scotsman, 11th July 1884

[15] The Scotsman, 18th October 1886

[16] Museum of the Scottish Shale Mine Industry (www.**scottishshale**.co.uk/ website)

[17] Dundee Courier, 13th July 1888

[18] Glasgow Herald, 18th July 1888

[19] Glasgow Herald, 7th December 1888

[20] Dunfermline Saturday Press, 29th October 1887

[21] Kinghorn Historical Society, Jim Allison, email from National Archive for Scotland, 25 October 2007)

[22] Register of the Great Seal of Scotland 1,(183), "Registrum Magni Sigili Regum Scotorum"

[23] Fife Herald, 19th August 1875

[24] Dundee Courier, 3rd July 1879

[25] Edinburgh Evening News, 13th November 1880

[26] Edinburgh Evening News, 8th October 1896

[27] Dundee Courier, 21st July 1910

[28] Dundee Courier, 11th May 1920

[29] Simpson's Mine, Burntisland
http://www.users.zetnet.co.uk/mmartin/fifepits/starter/east/pits/s/pit-10.htm